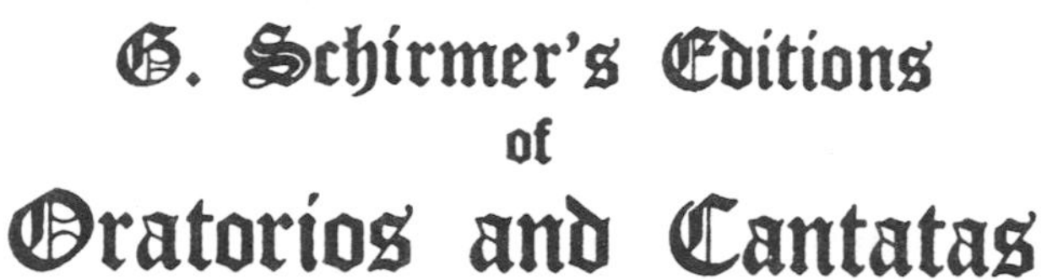
G. Schirmer's Editions
of
Oratorios and Cantatas

# MAGNIFICAT

For Soli, Chorus, and Orchestra

by

JOHANN SEBASTIAN BACH

Ed. 2034

Score for Voices with Organ
or Piano Accompaniment

G. SCHIRMER, *Inc.*

DISTRIBUTED BY
HAL•LEONARD CORPORATION
7777 W. BLUEMOUND RD. P.O. BOX 13819 MILWAUKEE, WI 53213

# CONTENTS



All the dynamic indications and tempo indications in brackets are suggestions by the editor.

# Magnificat

For Five-Part Chorus of Mixed Voices,
Soprano I, Soprano II, Alto, Tenor, and Bass Soli,
and Organ or Piano

Luke I: 46-55
English version by
Rev. J. Troutbeck, D.D.

Johann Sebastian Bach

## No. 1. Magnificat

My soul doth magnify the Lord

Chorus

Printed in the U.S.A.

f
f
f sempre
f
marcato
f
ff

SOPRANO I
Mag - - - ni - fi - cat, mag - ni - fi - cat,
My soul doth mag - ni - fy, doth mag - ni - fy,
SOPRANO II
Mag - - - ni - fi - cat, mag - ni - fi - cat,
My soul doth mag - ni - fy, doth mag - ni - fy,
ALTO
Mag - - - - ni - fi - cat,
My soul doth mag - ni - fy,
TENOR
Mag - - - ni - fi - cat,
My soul doth mag - ni - fy,
BASS
Mag - ni - fi - cat,
Doth mag - ni - fy,
f

6
mag-ni - fi-cat, mag - - -
doth mag - ni-fy, my soul ___ doth
mag-ni - fi-cat, mag - - -
doth mag - ni-fy, my soul ___ doth
mag-ni - fi-cat, mag - - - ni - fi-cat, mag-
doth mag - ni-fy, my soul ___ doth mag - ni-fy, doth
mag-ni - fi-cat, mag - - - ni - fi-cat, mag-
doth mag - ni-fy, my soul ___ doth mag - ni-fy, doth
mag-ni - fi-cat, mag - ni - fi-cat,
doth mag - ni-fy, doth mag - ni-fy,
f
f
ni - fi-cat, mag - ni-fi-cat a - ni-ma me - a, a - -
mag - ni-fy, my soul doth mag-ni-fy, my soul doth mag-ni-fy, mag - -
ni - fi-cat a - - ni-ma me - a, mag - ni - fi-
mag - ni-fy, mag - ni - fy, my soul doth mag - ni-
ni - fi-cat, mag - ni - fi-cat, mag - ni - fi-cat, mag - -
mag - ni-fy, doth mag - ni-fy, doth mag - ni-fy, my soul doth
ni - fi-cat, mag - ni - fi-cat, mag - ni - fi-cat, mag - -
mag - ni-fy, doth mag - ni-fy, doth mag - ni-fy, my soul doth
mag - - - - - - ni-fi-cat a - ni-ma
my soul ___ doth mag - ni - fy, ___ doth mag-ni-fy, mag - ni -
42689

- - - ni-ma me - a, a - ni-ma me - a, a - ni-ma
- - ni - fy the Lord, my_ soul doth mag-ni-fy, mag - ni -
cat, mag - ni - fi-cat a - ni-ma, a - - ni-ma me - a, a - - ni-ma
fy, my soul doth mag - ni - fy, doth mag - ni - fy, doth mag - ni -
ni - fi-cat, mag - - ni - fi-cat a - ni-ma me - a, a - ni-ma
mag - ni - fy, my soul doth mag - ni - fy, my_ soul doth mag-ni-fy, mag - ni -
ni - fi-cat, mag - - ni - fi-cat a - ni-ma me - a, mag-ni - fi-
mag - ni-fy, my soul doth mag - ni - fy, my_ soul doth mag-ni-fy, mag - ni-
me - a, a - ni-ma me - a, a - ni-ma me - a, a - ni-ma
fy, _ mag - ni - fy, _ my_ soul doth mag-ni-fy, mag - ni -
me - a Do - - - - - - - mi - num,
fy, doth mag - - - - ni - fy_ the Lord,
me - a, a - - ni-ma me - a Do - mi - num,
fy, my soul_ doth mag-ni - fy_ the_ Lord,
me - a, a - - ni-ma me - a Do - mi - num, mag - - -
fy, my soul_ doth mag-ni - fy_ the Lord, my soul_ doth
cat a - - ni - ma me - a Do - - mi - num, mag - - -
fy, my soul_ doth_ mag - ni - fy_ the Lord, my soul_ doth
me - a, a - - ni - ma me - a Do - mi - num,
fy, doth mag - ni - fy, mag - ni - fy the Lord,

mag - - - - ni - fi - cat, mag - ni - fi - cat,
my soul doth mag - ni - fy, doth mag - ni - fy,
mag - - - - ni - fi - cat, mag - ni - fi - cat,
my soul doth mag - ni - fy, doth mag - ni - fy,
ni - fi - cat, mag - ni - fi - cat, mag - ni - fi - cat,
mag - ni - fy, doth mag - ni - fy, doth mag - ni - fy,
ni - fi - cat, mag - ni - fi - cat, mag - ni - fi - cat,
mag - ni - fy, doth mag - ni - fy, doth mag - ni - fy,
mag - ni - fi - cat, mag - ni - fi - cat,
doth mag - ni - fy, doth mag - ni - fy,
f
f
mag - - ni - fi - cat, mag - ni - fi - cat,
my soul doth mag - ni - fy, doth mag - ni - fy,
mag - - ni - fi - cat, mag - ni - fi - cat,
my soul doth mag - ni - fy, doth mag - ni - fy,
mag - - ni - fi - cat,
my soul doth mag - ni - fy,
mag - - ni - fi - cat,
my soul doth mag - ni - fy,
mag - - ni - fi - cat,
my soul doth mag - ni - fy,
f
f

mag - - - - - - - ni - fi - cat, mag -
my soul doth mag - ni - fy, doth
mag - - ni - fi - cat, mag -
my soul doth mag - ni - fy, doth
mag - -
my soul
ni - fi - cat, mag - ni - fi - cat, mag - ni - fi - cat,
mag - ni - fy, doth mag - ni - fy, doth mag - ni - fy,
ni - fi - cat, mag - ni - fi - cat, mag - ni - fi - cat,
mag - ni - fy, doth mag - ni - fy, doth mag - ni - fy,
- - - - ni - fi - cat, mag - ni - fi - cat,
doth mag - ni - fy, doth mag - ni - fy,
mag - - - ni - fi - cat, mag - - -
my soul doth mag - ni - fy, my soul doth
mag - - - - - - - - - -
my soul doth
f
f
f
f
f
ff

mag - - - ni - fi-cat, mag-ni - fi - cat, mag-ni - fi-
my soul doth mag - ni-fy, doth mag - ni - fy, doth mag - ni-
mag-ni-fi-cat, mag-ni - fi-cat, mag-ni - fi - cat, mag-ni - fi-
my soul doth mag - ni-fy, doth mag - ni - fy, doth mag - ni-
mag - - - ni - fi-cat, mag-ni - fi - cat, mag-ni - fi-
my soul doth mag - ni-fy, doth mag - ni - fy, doth mag - ni-
ni - fi-cat, mag-ni - fi - cat, mag-ni - fi-
mag - ni-fy, doth mag - ni - fy, doth mag - ni-
ni - fi-cat, mag-ni-fi - cat, mag - - ni - fi -
mag - ni-fy, doth mag-ni - fy, my soul doth mag-ni -
ff
ff
cat, mag - ni - fi-cat,
fy, doth mag - ni-fy,
cat, mag - ni - fi-cat,
fy, doth mag - ni-fy,
cat, mag - - - ni - fi-cat, mag - ni - fi-cat,
fy, my soul doth mag - ni-fy, doth mag - ni-fy,
cat, mag - - - ni - fi-cat, mag - - -
fy, my soul doth mag - ni-fy, my soul doth
cat, mag - ni - fi - cat, mag - - -
fy, doth mag-ni-fy the Lord, my soul doth

mag - - - ni - fi - cat, mag -
my soul doth mag - ni - fy, doth
mag - - ni - fi - cat, mag -
my soul doth mag - ni - fy, doth
mag - ni - fi - cat, mag -
doth mag - ni - fy, doth
ni - fi - cat, mag - ni - fi - cat, mag -
mag - ni - fy, doth mag - ni - fy, doth
ni - fi - cat, mag - ni - fi - cat, mag - ni - fi -
mag - ni - fy, doth mag - ni - fy, doth mag - ni - fy the
ni - fi - cat, mag - ni - fi - cat, mag - ni - fi - cat, mag -
mag - ni - fy, doth mag - ni - fy, doth mag - ni - fy, my soul doth
ni - fi - cat, mag - ni - fi - cat a - ni - ma me - a, a -
mag - ni - fy, my soul doth mag - ni - fy, mag - ni - fy the Lord, mag -
ni - fi - cat a - - ni - ma me - a, mag - ni - fi -
mag - ni - fy, mag - - ni - fy, my soul doth mag - ni -
ni - fi cat, mag - ni - fi - cat, mag - ni - fi - cat, mag -
mag - ni - fy, doth mag - ni - fy, doth mag - ni - fy, my soul doth
cat, mag - - - ni - fi - cat a - ni - ma
Lord, my soul doth mag - ni - fy, doth mag - ni - fy, mag - ni -

ni - fi-cat, mag - ni - fi-cat a - ni-ma me - a, mag-ni - fi-
mag - ni-fy, my soul doth mag - ni-fy, my soul doth mag-ni-fy, doth mag - ni-
- - - - ni-ma me - a, a - ni-ma me - a, a - ni-ma
- - - - ni - fy,— my soul doth mag-ni-fy, mag - ni -
cat, mag - ni-fi-cat a-ni-ma, a - ni-ma me - a, a - ni-ma
fy, my soul doth mag-ni - fy, doth mag - ni - fy, doth mag - ni -
ni - fi-cat, mag - ni - fi-cat a - ni-ma me - a, a - ni-ma
mag - ni-fy, my soul doth mag - ni-fy, my soul doth mag-ni-fy, mag - ni -
me - a, a - ni-ma me - a, a - ni-ma me - a, a - ni-ma
fy, mag - ni - fy,— my soul doth mag-ni-fy, mag - ni -
cat a - ni - ma me - a Do - mi - num.
fy, my soul doth mag-ni-fy the Lord.
me - a Do - mi - num.
fy, doth mag - ni - fy the Lord.
me - a, a - ni-ma me - a Do - mi - num.
fy, my soul doth mag-ni - fy the Lord.
me - a, a - ni-ma me - a Do - mi - num.
fy, my soul doth mag-ni - fy the Lord.
me - a, a - ni - ma me - a Do - mi - num.
fy, my soul doth mag - ni - fy the Lord.

ff
ff

# No. 2. Et exultavit spiritus meus

## And my spirit hath rejoiced

### Alto Solo

et ex - ul - ta - vit spi - ri - tus me - us, et ex - ul -
hath re - joic - ed in God, my Sav - iour, hath re -
dim.
p
pp
ta - - - - - - - vit spi - ri - tus me -
joic - - - - - - - ed in God, re - joic - ed in
us: in De - - - o sa - lu - ta - - - ri, sa - lu -
God, re - joic - - - ed, re - joic - - - ed, re -
pp
ta - - - - - - - - - - - - -
joic - - - - - - - - - - - - -
p

ri me-o, in De-o sa-lu-ta ri me-o.
ed in God, re-joic-ed in God, my Sav-iour,
mf
Et ex-ul-ta-vit spi-ri-tus me-us: in De-
and my spir-it hath re-joic-ed, re-joic-
dim.
p
o sa-lu-ta-ri, sa-lu-ta-
ed, hath re-joic-ed, re-joic-ed in God, in God,
pp

tr
- ri me - o, in De - - o sa - lu- ta - ri,
my Sav - iour, hath re - joic-ed in God, my Sav-iour,
pp
in De - o sa - lu - ta - ri me - o, in De - o sa - lu - ta -
hath re - joic - ed in God, my Sav - iour, in God, my Sav-iour, my
cresc.
dim.
ri me - o.
Sav - iour.
mf
cresc.

No. 3. Quia respexit
For He hath regarded
Soprano Solo
[Adagio ♪ = 69]
pp
Soprano Solo
Qui - a re - spex - it
For He hath re - gard - ed,
p
hu - mi - li - ta - tem, hu - mi - li - ta - tem an -
re - gard - ed the low - li - ness, re - gard - ed the low - li - ness of
cil - læ su - æ,
His hand - maid - en,

qui - a re - spex - it hu - mi - li - ta - tem,
for He hath re - gard - ed, re - gard - ed the low - li - ness,
low estate
hu - mi - li - ta - tem an - cil - læ su - æ:
re - gard-ed the low - li - ness of His hand-maid - en.
low estate
tr
cresc.
p
ec - ce, ec - ce,
for Be-hold, from hence-forth,
Generationem
ec - ce, ec - ce,
for be-hold, from hence-forth,
ec - ce e - nim ex hoc be -
from hence-forth all gen - er -

## No. 4. Omnes generationes

### For behold, all generations

Chorus

o - - - - - - - - - - - - - - -
a - - - - - - - - - - - - - - -
ge - ne - ra - ti - o - - - - - - - nes, om - nes,
gen - - er - a - - - - - - - tions, for be -
om - nes, om - nes ge - ne - ra - ti - o - nes,
for be - hold, all gen - - er - a - tions,
om - nes, om - nes ge - ne - ra - ti - o - - -
for be - hold, all gen - - er - a - - -
- - nes, om - nes, om - nes ge - ne - ra - ti -
- - tions, for be - hold, all gen - - er -
- - - - - nes, om - nes, om - nes ge - ne - ra - ti -
- - - - - tions, for be - hold, all gen - - er -
om - - - nes, om - nes ge - ne - ra - ti - o - - -
hold, be - hold, all gen - - er - a - - -
om - nes, om - nes ge - ne - ra - ti - o - - - - -
for be - hold, all gen - - er - a - - - - -
- - - - - nes,
- - - - - tions,
o - nes, om - - - nes, om - nes
a - tions, for be - hold, be - hold, all

o - - - - nes, om - - - - nes, om - nes
a - - - - tions, for be - hold, all
- - - - - - - - - nes, om - nes ge - ne - ra - ti -
- - - - - - - - - tions, be - hold, all gen - - er -
- nes, om - nes ge - ne - ra - ti - o - - - - - - -
tions, be - hold, all gen - - er - a - - - - - - -
om - - - nes, om - nes ge - ne - ra - ti - o - - -
for be - hold, all gen - - er - a - - -
ge - ne - ra - ti - o - - - - - - - - - -
gen - - er - a - - - - - - - - - - -
ge - ne - ra - ti - o - - nes, om - nes, om - nes
gen - - er - a - - tions, for be - hold, all
o - - - - - - nes,
a - - - - - - tions,
- - - - - - - nes,
- - - - - - - tions,
- - - - - - nes,
- - - - - - tions,
- - - - - - - nes, om-nes, om - nes ge - ne - ra - ti -
- - - - - - - tions, for be-hold, all gen - - er -

ge - ne - ra - ti - o - - - - - - - nes,
gen - - er - a - - - - - - - tions,
om - nes, om - nes ge - ne - ra - ti - o - - - -
for be - hold, all gen - - er - a - - - -
om - nes, om - nes
for be hold, all
om - nes, om - nes ge - ne - ra - ti - o - - - - - - -
for be - hold, all gen - - er - a - - - - - - -
o - - - nes, om - nes, om - nes ge - ne - ra - ti -
a - - - tions, for be - hold, all gen - - er -
om - nes, om - nes ge - ne - ra - ti - o - - - - - -
for be - hold, all gen - - er - a - - - - - -
- - - - - nes, om - nes, om - nes ge - ne - ra - ti -
- - - - - tions, for be - hold, all gen - - er -
ge - ne - ra - ti - o - - - - - - - nes,
gen - - er - a - - - - - - - tions,
- nes, om - nes, om - nes ge - ne - ra - ti - o - - -
- tions, for be - hold, all gen - - er - a - - -
o - - - - - - - nes, om - nes, om - nes
a - - - - - - - tions, for be - hold, all

- nes, om - nes ge - ne - ra - ti - o - nes, om - nes, om - nes
tions, be - hold, all gen - - er - a - tions, for be - hold, all
o - - - - - - nes, om - nes ge - ne - ra - ti -
a - - - - - - tions, be - hold, all gen - - er -
om - nes, om - nes ge - ne - ra - ti - o - - - -
for be - hold, all gen - - er - a - - - -
- - - - - - - nes,
- - - - - - - tions,
ge - ne - ra - ti - o - - - - - - - - - - - -
gen - - er - a - - - - - - - - - - - -
ge - ne - ra - ti - o - - - - - - nes, om - - nes, om - nes
gen - - er - a - - - - - - tions, for be - hold, all
o - - nes, om - nes, om - nes ge - ne - ra - ti -
a - - tions, for be - hold, all gen - - er -
- - - - - - - - - - - - - - nes,
- - - - - - - - - - - - - - tions,
om - nes, om - nes ge - ne - ra - ti - o - - - - -
for be - hold, all gen - - er - a - - - - -
- nes, om - nes, om - nes ge - ne - ra - ti - o - - -
- tions, for be - hold, all gen - - er - a - - -

ge - ne - ra - ti - o - - - - nes, ge - ne - ra - ti - o -
gen - - er - a - - - - - tions, gen - er - a -
o - - - - - - - - nes, ge - ne - ra - ti - o -
a - - - - - - - - tions, gen - er - a -
om - nes, om - nes ge - ne - ra - ti - o - - - - - -
for be - hold, all gen - - er - a - - - - - -
- nes, om - nes ge - ne - ra - ti - o -
- tions, for be - hold, all gen - er - a -
- - - - nes, om - nes ge - ne - ra - ti - o - -
- - - - tions, be - hold, all gen - - er - a - -
nes, om-nes, om - nes ge - ne - ra - ti -
tions, for be-hold, all gen - - er -
nes, om-nes, om - nes ge - ne - ra - ti - o -
tions, for be - hold, all gen - - er - a -
nes, om-nes, om - nes ge - ne - ra - ti - o - - -
tions, for be-hold, all gen - - er - a - - -
nes, om-nes, om - nes ge - ne - ra - ti - o - - - - -
tions, for be-hold, all gen - - er - a - - - -
nes, om-nes, om - nes ge - ne - ra - ti - o - - - nes,
tions, for be-hold, all gen - - er - a - - - tions,
ff ff ff ff

o - - - - - - - - - - - nes, om - nes, om - nes
a - - - - - - - - - - - tions, for be - hold, all
om - nes, om - nes ge - ne - ra - ti - o - nes,
for be - hold, be - hold, all gen - er - a - tions,
ff
ge - ne - ra - ti - o - nes, om - nes, om - nes ge - ne - ra - ti - o - nes.
gen - er - a - tions, all, be - hold, all gen - er - a - tions.
om - - - - nes ge - ne - ra - ti - o - nes.
all, all gen - er - a - tions.
om - nes, om - nes ge - ne - ra - ti - o - - - - - - - - nes.
for be - hold, all gen - er - a - - - - - - - - tions.
tr

## No. 5. Quia fecit mihi magna

### For He that is mighty

**Bass Solo**

est, qui-a fe-cit mi-hi mag - - - -
me, for He that is might - - - -
p dolce
- na qui po - - - tens est: et sanc-tum no - men
- y hath mag - - ni-fi-ed me, and ho-ly is His
dim.
p
e-jus, et sanc - - - - - tum no-men, et
name, and ho - - - - ly, and ho-ly, and
sanc-tum no-men e-jus, sanc - - tum no-men e-jus, sanc-tum
ho-ly is His name, and ho - - ly is His name, and ho-ly

no - men__ e-jus, et sanc - tum no-men e - jus.
is His name,and ho-ly, and ho - - ly, ho-ly is His name,
p
Qui-a fe-cit mi-hi mag - na qui po - tens est: et sanc - -
for_ He_ that is might-y hath mag-ni-fi-ed me,and ho - -
p
mf
p
- - tum no-men, sanc - tum no-men e - jus.
- ly is His name, and ho - - ly_ is His name.
dolce
pp
cresc.
mf
p
cresc.

# No. 6. Et misericordia

## And His mercy is on them

### Duet for Alto and Tenor

es,
tions,
es,
tions,
mp
et mi - se - ri - cor - di - a, mi - se - ri -
and His mer - cy is on them, on them that
et mi - se - ri - cor - di - a, mi - se - ri -
and His mer - cy is on them, on them that
p
cor - di - a a pro - ge - ni - e in pro - ge - ni - es, in pro - ge - ni -
fear Him, through-out all, through-out all gen - er - a - tions, all gen - er - a -
cor - di - a a pro - ge - ni - e in pro - ge - ni -
fear Him, through-out all, through-out all gen - er - a -

es ti - men - ti - bus e - um, ti - men - - ti - bus
tions, on them ___ that fear Him, on them ___ that
es ti - men - - ti - bus e - um, ti - men - ti - bus
tions, on them ___ that fear Him, on them ___ that
e - um, et mi - se - ri -
fear Him, and His mer - cy
e - um, et mi - se - ri -
fear Him, and His mer - cy
mf
p
cor - di - a, ___ mi - se - ri - cor - di - a ___ a pro - ge - ni - e
is ___ on them, ___ on them that fear ___ Him ___ through-out all, through-out
cor - di - a, ___ mi - se - ri - cor - di - a ___ a pro - ge - -
is ___ on them, ___ on them that fear ___ Him ___ through-out all, ___

in progenies, in progenies timentibus
all generations, all generations, on them that
nie in progenies timentibus
throughout all generations, on them that
eum, timentibus
fear Him, on them that
eum, timentibus
fear Him, on them that
eum, timentibus, timentibus, ti-
fear Him throughout all generations, all generations, all
eum, timentibus, timentibus, ti-
fear Him throughout all generations, all generations, all
p

## No. 7. Fecit potentiam

### The Lord hath showed strength

Chorus

ti - am in bra - chi - o
ed strength with His
fe - cit po - ten - ti - am, fe - cit po - ten - ti - am,
the Lord hath show - ed strength, the Lord hath show - ed strength,
fe - po - ten - ti - am, fe - cit po - ten - ti - am,
the Lord hath show - ed strength, the Lord hath show - ed strength,
fe - cit po - ten
the Lord hath show
su - o, po - ten - ti - am, fe - cit po - ten - ti - am,
arm, the Lord hath show - ed strength, the Lord hath show - ed strength,
fe - cit po - ten - ti - am, fe - cit po - ten - ti - am,
the Lord hath show - ed strength, the Lord hath show - ed strength,

- - - - - - - - - - - ti - am in bra - - chi - o
- - - - - - - - - - - ed strength with His
in bra - - chi - o su - - o, dis - per - - - - -
hath show - ed strength, and scat - - - - -
fe - cit po - ten - ti - am, fe - cit po - ten - ti - am,
the Lord hath show - ed strength, the Lord hath show - ed strength,
fe - cit po - ten - - - - - - - - - - -
the Lord hath show - - - - - - - - - - -
su - o, po - ten - ti - am, fe - cit po - ten - ti - am
arm, the Lord hath show - ed strength, the Lord hath show - ed strength,
- sit, fe - cit po - ten - ti - am, fe - cit po - ten - ti - am, dis -
- tered, the Lord hath show - ed strength, the Lord hath show - ed strength, and
fe - cit po - ten - ti - am, fe - cit po - ten - ti - am,
the Lord hath show - ed strength, the Lord hath show - ed strength,

ti - am in bra - chi - o
ed strength with His
in bra - chi - o su - o, dis - per
hath show - ed strength, and scat
per - sit, dis - per - sit, dis - per
scat - tered, and scat - tered, and scat
fe - cit po - ten - ti - am, fe - cit po - ten - ti - am,
the Lord hath show - ed strength, the Lord hath show - ed strength,
su - o, po - ten - ti - am, fe - cit po - ten - ti - am
arm, the Lord hath show - ed strength, the Lord hath show - ed strength,
sit, fe - cit po - ten - ti - am, fe - cit po - ten - ti - am, dis -
tered, the Lord hath show - ed strength, the Lord hath show - ed strength, and
sit, fe - cit po - ten - ti - am, fe - cit po - ten - ti - am, dis -
tered, the Lord hath show - ed strength, the Lord hath show - ed strength, and
fe - cit po - ten
the Lord hath show

in bra - - chi-o su - - o, dis - per - - - - -
hath show - ed strength, and scat - - - - -
per - - - sit, dis-per - sit, dis - per - - - - -
scat - - - - tered, and scat - tered, and scat - - - - -
per - sit, dis - per - sit, dis - per - sit, dis - per - - -
scat - tered, and scat - tered, and scat-tered, and scat - - -
- - - - - - - - - ti - am in bra - - chi-o
- - - - - - - - - ed strength with His
fe - cit po - ten - - - - - - - - -
the Lord hath show - - - - - - - - - -
- sit, fe-cit po-ten - ti-am, fe - cit po - ten - ti-am, dis -
- tered, the Lord hath show - ed strength, the Lord hath show - ed strength, and
- sit, fe-cit po - ten - ti-am, fe - cit po - ten - ti-am, dis -
- tered, the Lord hath show - ed strength, the Lord hath show - ed strength, and
- sit, fe-cit po - ten - ti-am, fe - cit po - ten - ti-am,
- tered, the Lord hath show - ed strength, the Lord hath show - ed strength,
su - o, fe-cit po - ten - ti-am, fe - cit po - ten - ti-am
arm, the Lord hath show - ed strength, the Lord hath show - ed strength,

- - - - - - - - - - ti - am in bra - chi-o
- - - - - - - - - - ed strength with His
per - - - sit, dis-per - sit, dis - per - - - - -
scat - - - tered, and scat-tered, and scat - - - - -
per - sit, dis - per - sit, dis - per - sit, dis - per - - - -
scat - tered, and scat - tered, and scat - tered, and scat - - - -
dis - per - sit, dis - per - sit, dis - per - sit, dis - per - sit,
and scat - tered, and scat - tered, and scat - tered, and scat - tered,
in bra - chi - o su - o, dis - per - - - - -
hath show - ed strength, and scat - - - - -
su - o, po - ten - ti - am, fe - cit po - ten - ti - am
arm, the Lord hath show - ed strength, the Lord hath show - ed strength,
- sit, fe - cit po - ten - ti - am, fe - cit po - ten - ti - am, dis -
- tered, the Lord hath show - ed strength, the Lord hath show - ed strength, and
- sit, fe - cit po - ten - ti - am, fe - cit po - ten - ti - am, dis -
- tered, the Lord hath show - ed strength, the Lord hath show - ed strength, and
fe - cit po - ten - ti - am, fe - cit po - ten - ti - am, dis -
the Lord hath show - ed strength, the Lord hath show - ed strength, and
- sit, fe - cit po - ten - ti - am, fe - cit po - ten - ti - am,
- tered, the Lord hath show - ed strength, the Lord hath show - ed strength,
ff

in bra - chi - o su - o, dis - per - - - - -
hath show - ed strength, and scat - - - - -
per - sit, dis - per - sit, dis - per - sit, dis - per - - -
scat - tered, and scat - tered, and scat - tered, and scat - - -
per - - - sit, dis - per - sit, dis - per - - - - -
scat - - - tered, and scat - tered, and scat - - - - -
per - sit, dis - per - sit, dis - per - sit, dis - per - sit, dis -
scat - tered, and scat - tered, and scat - tered, and scat - tered, and
dis - per - sit, dis - per - sit, dis - per - sit, dis - per - sit,
and scat - tered, and scat - tered, and scat - tered, and scat - tered,
- - - - - sit, dis - per - sit, dis - per - sit,
- - - - - tered, and scat - tered, and scat - tered,
- sit, dis - per - - - - - sit, dis - per - sit,
- tered, and scat - - - - - tered, and scat - tered,
- - - - - - - - - sit, dis - per - sit, dis -
- - - - - - - - - tered, and scat - tered, and
per - - - - - sit, dis - per - sit, dis -
scat - - - - - tered, and scat - tered, and
dis - per - - - - - sit, dis - per - sit,
and scat - - - - - tered, and scat - tered,

dis - per - sit su - per - bos
and scat - tered the proud
dis - per - sit su - per - bos
and scat - tered the proud
per - sit, dis - per - sit su - per - bos
scat - tered, and scat - tered the proud
per - sit, dis - per - sit su - per - bos
scat - tered, and scat - tered the proud
dis - per - sit su - per - bos
and scat - tered the proud
ff
Adagio [♩ = 50]
men - te cor - dis su - i, men - te cor - dis su - i.
in the im - ag - i - na - tion of their hearts, of their hearts.
men - te cor - dis su - i, men - te cor - dis su - i.
in the im - ag - i - na - tion of their hearts, of their hearts.
men - te cor - dis su - i, men - te cor - dis su - i.
in the im - ag - i - na - tion of their hearts, of their hearts.
men - te cor - dis su - i, men - te cor - dis su - i.
in the im - ag - i - na - tion of their hearts, of their hearts.
men - te cor - dis su - i, men - te cor - dis su - i.
in the im - ag - i - na - tion of their hearts, of their hearts.
Adagio [♩ = 50]
f
tr

## No. 8. Deposuit potentes

### He hath put down the mighty

**Tenor Solo**

Tenor Solo
De - po - - -
He hath
dim.
p
- su - it, de - po - - - - - su - it po -
— put down, He hath put down the
ten - - - - tes de se - - - - -
might - - - - y from their thrones,
- - de, et ex - al - ta - - - - - - -
and hath ex - alt - - - - - - -

vit hu - mi -
ed them of low de -
les,
gree.
mf
de -
He
po - su - it, de - po -
hath put down, He hath
p

- su - it po - ten - - - tes de
— put down the might - - - y from their
se - - - - de, et ex - al - ta - - -
thrones, and hath ex - alt - -
- - - - - - - - - - - vit, et ex - al -
- - - - - - - - - - - ed, ex - alt ed
cresc.
ta - vit hu - mi - les,
them of low de - gree,

et ex - al - ta - - - - -
and hath ex - alt - - - - - ed
- vit hu - mi - les.
them of low de - gree.
mf
fz

# No. 9. Esurientes implevit bonis

## He hath filled the hungry

### Alto Solo

di - vi - tes di - mi - sit, et di - vi - tes di - mi - sit, di -
rich hath sent emp-ty a-way,— the rich hath sent emp-ty a-way,— hath
mi - sit in - a - nes, et di - vi - tes di - mi - - sit in -
sent— a - way,— the rich hath sent emp-ty a-way,— a -
p dolce
a - nes, di - mi - sit in - a - nes,
way,— sent emp-ty a-way.—
tr
mf
dim.
e - su - ri - en-tes im -
He hath fill - ed the hun-gry, the
p

ple - - vit bo - nis, e - su - ri - en - tes im -
hun - gry with good things, He hath fill - ed the hun - gry, hath
ple - - vit bo - - - - - - - - - - -
fill - ed the hun - - - - - - - - - -
- - - nis, im - ple - - - - - - - -
- - - gry, the hun - - - - - - - -
- - - - - - - - - - - - - vit
- - - - - - - - - - gry with good

bo-nis, et di - vi - tes di - mi - sit, et di - vi - tes_ di -
things, and the rich hath sent emp-ty a - way,__ the rich hath sent emp-ty a -
mi - sit, di - mi - - sit in - a - nes, di - mi - sit in -
way,__ hath sent____ emp - ty, sent emp - ty a - way,__ a -
a - nes, di-mi - sit in - a - nes.
way,__ the rich hath sent emp-ty a - way.
p
mf
tr
rit.
pp

# No. 10. Suscepit Israel

## His servant, Israel

Trio for Soprano I, Soprano II, and Alto

sus - ce - pit Is - ra - el pu - e - rum su - um, sus - ce - pit,
His ser - vant, Is - ra - el, He hath hol - pen, hath hol - pen,
Is - ra - el, sus - ce - pit Is - ra - el, sus - ce - pit Is -
Is - ra - el, His ser - vant, Is - ra - el, His ser - vant, Is -
su - um, sus - ce - pit Is - ra - el, sus - ce - pit
hol - pen, His ser - vant, Is - ra - el, His ser - vant,
p
sus - ce - pit Is - ra - el pu - e - rum su - um:
His ser - vant, Is - ra - el, He hath hol - pen,
- ra - el pu - e - rum su - um:
- ra - el, He hath hol - pen,
Is - ra - el pu - e - rum su - um: re - cor -
Is - ra - el, He hath hol - pen, in re -

re - cor - da - tus mi - se - ri - cor - - - - - -
in_ re - mem - brance of_ His mer - - - - - - -
re - cor - da - tus mi - se - ri - cor - -
in_ re - mem - brance of___ His mer - -
da - tus mi - se - ri - cor - - - - - - - - -
mem-brance of His mer - - - - - - - - -
- - - - - di - æ su - æ, re - cor - da - tus mi -
- - - - - cy, His mer - cy, in_ re - mem - brance,
- - di - æ, re - cor - da - tus mi - se - ri - cor - di -
- - - cy, in_ re - mem - brance,_ in re - mem - -
- - - - - di - æ, re - cor - da - tus mi - se - ri -
- - - - - cy, in_ re - mem-brance, re - mem - brance

- se - ri - cor - - - - di - æ su - æ, mi -
in re - mem - - - - brance of His
æ, mi - - - se - ri - cor - - - - - -
- brance of His mer - - - - - -
cor - - - - di - æ, mi - se - ri - cor - -
of His mer - cy, in re - mem - -
se - ri - cor - - - - - di - æ su - æ.
mer - - - - - - cy, His mer - cy.
- - - - - - di - æ su - - æ.
- - - - - - cy, His mer - - - cy.
- di - æ mi - se - ri - cor - di - æ su - æ.
- - brance of His mer - cy, His mer - - cy.

# No. 11. Sicut locutus est

## Even as He promised

Chorus

f
Si - cut lo - cu - tus est ad pa - tres nos -
Ev'n as He prom - is - ed to our fore - fa -
nos - tros, A - bra - ham et se - mi - ni e - jus in se - cu -
fa - thers, to A - bra - ham and to his seed for - ev -
se - cu - la, si - cut lo - cu - tus est in se - cu -
ev - er, ev'n as He prom - is - ed, for - ev -
se - cu - la, si - cut lo - cu - tus est ad pa - tres nos -
ev - er, ev'n as He prom - is - ed to our fore - fa -
f
Si - cut lo -
Ev'n as He
tros, A - bra - ham et se - mi - ni e - jus in se - cu - la, A - bra -
thers, to A - bra - ham and to his seed for - ev - er, to A - bra -
la, in se - cu - la, in se - cu - la,
er, for - ev - er, for - ev - er,
la, si - cut lo - cu - tus est ad pa - tres nos - tros, si - cut lo -
er, ev'n as He prom - is - ed to our fore - fa - thers, ev'n as He
tros, si - cut lo - cu - tus est in se - cu - la,
thers, ev'n as He prom - is - ed, for - ev - er,

cu - tus est ad pa-tres nos - tros, A - bra-ham et se-mi-ni
prom - is - ed to our fore-fa - thers, to A - bra-ham and to his
ham et se-mi-ni e - jus in se - cu - la, si-cut lo - cu - tus
ham and to his seed for - ev - er, ev'n as He prom - is -
si - cut lo - cu - tus
ev'n as He prom - is -
cu - tus est in se - cu - la,
prom - is - ed, for - ev - er,
e - jus in se - cu - la, si-cut lo - cu - tus est in
seed for - ev - er, ev'n as He prom - is - ed, for -
est ad pa-tres nos - tros in se - cu - la, ad pa - tres
ed to our fore-fa - thers, for - ev - er, to our fore-
est ad pa - tres nos - tros, A - bra-ham et se-mi-ni e - jus in
ed to our fore - fa - thers, to A - bra-ham and to his seed for -
si - cut lo - cu - tus est ad pa - tres
ev'n as He prom - is - ed to our fore-

se - cu - la, si - cut lo - cu - tus est in se - cu -
ev - er, ev'n as He prom - is - ed, for - ev -
nos - tros, si - cut lo - cu - tus est ad pa - tres nos -
fa - thers, ev'n as He prom - is - ed to our fore - fa -
se - cu - la, si - cut lo - cu - tus est in se - cu -
ev - er, ev'n as He prom - is - ed, for - ev -
nos - tros, A - bra - ham et se - mi - ni e - jus in se - cu -
fa - thers, to A - bra - ham and to his seed for - ev -
si - cut lo - cu - tus est ad pa - tres nos -
ev'n as He prom - is - ed to our fore - fa -
la, A - bra - ham et se - mi - ni e - jus, A - bra - ham et se - mi - ni
er, to A - bra - ham and to his seed, to A - bra - ham and to his
tros, A - bra - ham, A - bra - ham et se - mi - ni e - jus, A - bra-
thers, to A - bra - ham, to A - bra - ham and to his seed, to A - bra-
la. A - bra - ham, A - bra - ham et se - mi - ni e - jus, A - bra-
er, to A - bra - ham, to A - bra - ham and to his seed, to A - bra-
la, A - bra - ham, A - bra - ham et se - mi - ni e - jus, A - bra-
er, to A - bra - ham, to A - bra - ham and to his seed, to A - bra-
tros, A - bra - ham, A - bra - ham et se - mi - ni e - jus, A - bra-
thers, to A - bra - ham, to A - bra - ham and to his seed, to A - bra-

e - jus in se - - - - - - - - - -
seed for - ev - - - - - - - - - -
ham et se-mi-ni e - jus in se - - - - - - cu -
ham and to his_ seed for - ev - - - - - - -
ham et se-mi-ni e - jus in se - - - - cu -
ham and to his_ seed for - ev - - - - -
ham et se-mi-ni e - jus in se - - - - cu -
ham and to his_ seed for - ev - - - - -
ham et se-mi-ni e - jus, se-mi-ni e - jus, se-mi-ni e - jus in se-cu -
ham and to his_ seed, and to his_ seed, and to his_ seed for - ev -
- - - - - cu - la, in se - cu -
- - - - - - - er, for - ev -
la, in se - - - - - - - - cu -
er, for - ev - - - - - - - - -
la, A - bra-ham et se-mi-ni e - jus in se - cu -
er, to A - bra-ham and to his_ seed for - ev -
la, in se - - - cu -
er, for - ev - - - - -
la, si-cut lo - cu - tus est ad pa-tres nos - -
er, ev'n as He prom - is - ed to our fore - fa - -

la, A-bra-ham et se-mi-ni e - jus in se - cu - la.
er, to A-bra-ham and to his_ seed for - ev - - er.
la, A-bra-ham et_ se-mi-ni e - jus in se - cu - la.
er, to A-bra-ham and to his_ seed for - ev - - er.
la, A-bra-ham et se-mi-ni e - jus in se - - cu - la.
er, to A-bra-ham and to his seed for - ev - - - er.
la, A-bra-ham et se-mi-ni e - jus in se - cu - la.
er, to A-bra-ham and to his_ seed for - ev - - - er.
tros, A-bra-ham et se - mi-ni e - jus in se - cu - la.
thers, to A-bra-ham and to_ his_ seed_ for - ev - er.
No. 12. Gloria Patri
Glory to the Father
[Allegro moderato ♩ = 80]
Chorus
Glo-ri-a,
Glo - ry,
Glo-ri-a, glo -
Glo - ry, glo -
Glo-ri-a, glo -
Glo - ry, glo -
Glo-ri-a, glo -
Glo - ry, glo -
Glo-ri-a, glo -
Glo - ry, glo -
[Allegro moderato ♩ = 80]

glo - - - - - ri - a Pa - tri, glo - - - - -
glo - - - - - ry to the Fa - ther, glo - - - - -
- - - - - - ri - a Pa - tri,
- - - - - - ry to the Fa - ther,
- - - - - - ri - a Pa - tri, glo - -
- - - - - - ry to the Fa - ther, glo - -
- - - - - - ri - a Pa - tri,
- - - - - - ry to the Fa - ther,
- - - - - - ri - a Pa - tri,
- - - - - - ry to the Fa - ther,
cresc.
ff
f
- - - - - - - - - - - - - - ri - a
- - - - - - - - - - - - - - ry to the
glo - - - - - - - - - - ri - a
glo - - - - - - - - - - ry to the
- - - - - - - - - - - - - ri - a
- - - - - - - - - - - - - ry to the
glo - - - - - - - - - ri - a
glo - - - - - - - - - ry to the
glo - - - - - - ri - a
glo - - - - - - ry to the
cresc.
ff

Fi - li - o,
Son,
glo
ri - a et Spi - ri - tu - i
ry to the Ho - ly Ghost, the
ff
f
cresc.
ff sempre

Tempo I°
Sanc - to!
Ho - ly Ghost!
Sanc - to!
Ho - ly Ghost!
Sanc - to!
Ho - ly Ghost!
Sanc - to!
Ho - ly Ghost!
Sanc - to!
Ho - ly Ghost!
Tempo I°
Si-cut e-rat in prin-
As it was in the be-
Si-cut e-rat in prin-
As it was in the be-
Si-cut e-rat in prin - ci - pi - o,
As it was in the be-gin - ning,
Si-cut e-rat in prin - ci - pi - o,
As it was in the be-gin - ning,
Si-cut e - rat in prin -
As it was in the be -

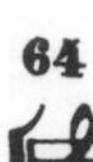

ci - pi - o,
gin - ning,
ci - pi - o,
gin - ning,
si - cut e - rat in - prin -
as it was in the be -
si - cut e - rat in prin -
as it was in the be -
ci - pi - o,
gin - ning,
si - cut e - rat in prin -
as it was in the be -
si - cut e - rat in prin - ci - pi - o, in prin - ci - pi - o, et
as it was in the be - gin - ning, as it was and is
si - cut e - rat in prin - ci - pi - o, in prin - ci - pi - o, et
as it was in the be - gin - ning, as it was and is
ci - pi - o, in prin - ci - pi - o, in prin - ci - pi - o, et
gin - ning, in the be - gin - ning, as it was and is
ci - pi - o, in prin - ci - pi - o, in prin - ci - pi - o, et
gin - ning, in the be - gin - ning, as it was and is
ci - pi - o, in prin - ci - pi - o, in prin - ci - pi - o, et
gin - ning, in the be - gin - ning, as it was and is

nunc, nunc et sem-per et in se - cu-la,
now, is now, and ev - er shall be,
nunc, nunc et sem-per et in se - cu-la,
now, is now, and ev - er shall be,
nunc, nunc et sem-per et in se - cu-la,
now, is now, and ev - er shall be,
nunc, nunc et sem-per et in se - cu-la,
now, is now, and ev - er shall be,
nunc, nunc et sem-per et in se - cu-la,
now, is now, and ev - er shall be,
et in se-cu-la se-cu - lo
world with-out end. A -
et in se-cu-la se-cu - lo
world with-out end. A -
et in se-cu-la se-cu - lo
world with-out end. A -
et in se-cu-la se-cu - lo
world with-out end. A -
et in se-cu-la se-cu-
world with-out end. A -

lo
rum. A - men.
men, A - men.
rum. A - men.
men, A - men.
rum. A - men.
men, A - men.
rum. A - men.
men, A - men.
rum. A - men.
men, A - men.
f